THE LITTLE WORLD OF
ELVES · & ·
FAIRIES

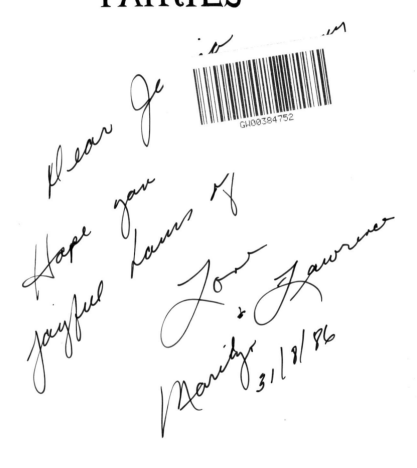

Dear Je...

Hope you

joyful hours of

Love
&
Lawrence

Marilyn 31/8/86

GW00384752

THE LITTLE WORLD OF

ELVES · &·
FAIRIES

AN ANTHOLOGY OF VERSE
WITH ILLUSTRATIONS BY
IDA RENTOUL OUTHWAITE

ANGUS
& ROBERTSON
PUBLISHERS

ANGUS & ROBERTSON PUBLISHERS

Unit 4, Eden Park, 31 Waterloo Road,
North Ryde, NSW, Australia 2113, and
16 Golden Square, London W1R 4BN,
United Kingdom

First published in Australia
by Angus & Robertson Publishers in 1985
First published in the United Kingdom
by Angus & Robertson (UK) Ltd in 1985

Copyright © Text selection and presentation
Angus & Robertson Publishers, 1985
© Illustrations Lady W. Martin, 1960
Illustrations photographed by Ralph Wayment
and reproduced from copies of *Elves and Fairies*
and *Fairyland* held by the Mitchell Library,
State Library of New South Wales

National Library of Australia
Cataloguing-in-publication data.

The little world of elves & fairies.

ISBN 0 207 15184 9
ISBN 0 207 14950 X (pbk.)

1. Children's poetry, English.
I. Outhwaite, Ida Rentoul, 1888-1960.

821'.008'09282

Printed in Australia by
The Dominion Press-Hedges & Bell

Preface

Ida Rentoul was born in Melbourne in 1888. Though denied formal training — her father believed art school would spoil her natural ability — she was encouraged at home and in 1903, when only fifteen, had several fairy drawings published in *The New Idea,* and had designed and illustrated a series of Christmas cards for which her father wrote the verse.

Her first book, *Mollie's Bunyip,* was published when she was the grand old age of sixteen and was quickly followed by others, in collaboration with her sister Annie, who wrote many of the books Ida illustrated.

In 1909 she married writer Grenbry Outhwaite and thereafter signed her work Ida Rentoul Outhwaite. One of the first works to bear her married name was the magnificent *Elves and Fairies,* published in a limited edition of 800 copies in 1916 and celebrated in 1985 by Australia Post. For the first time Ida's delightful watercolours were reproduced in full colour, all of them illustrating verses written by Annie. With the publication of this edition she was to attract worldwide interest in her work.

Ten years later she illustrated a companion volume entitled *Fairyland,* which again contained verse by Annie but also included prose by her husband. Like *Elves and Fairies, Fairyland* was a great success with the critics both at home and overseas, but it too was published in a limited edition of only 1000 copies. Thus the magic of Ida Rentoul Outhwaite's most beautiful work was known by relatively few people.

This edition contains illustrations from both these magnificent books and combines them with some of the best-loved fairy verse in the English language.

OVER HILL, OVER DALE

Over hill, over dale,
  Thorough bush, thorough brier,
Over park, over pale,
  Thorough flood, thorough fire:
I do wander everywhere,
Swifter than the moones sphere;
And I serve the fairy queen,
To dew her orbs upon the green.

The cowslips tall her pensioners be;
In their gold coats spots you see;
Those be rubies, fairy favours,
In those freckles live their savours:
I must go seek some dew-drops here,
And hang a pearl in every cowslip's ear.

William Shakespeare

FOREIGN LANDS

Up into the cherry tree
Who should climb but little me?
I held the trunk with both my hands
And looked abroad on foreign lands.

I saw the next door garden lie,
Adorned with flowers, before my eye,
And many pleasant places more
That I had never seen before.

I saw the dimpling river pass
And be the sky's blue looking-glass;
The dusty roads go up and down
With people tramping in to town.

If I could find a higher tree
Farther and farther I should see,
To where the grown-up river slips
Into the sea among the ships,

To where the roads on either hand
Lead onward into fairy land,
Where all the children dine at five,
And all the playthings come alive.

Robert Louis Stevenson

THE FAIRY MAN

It was, it was a fairy man
    Who came to town to-day;
"I'll make a cake for sixpence
    If you will pay, will pay."

I paid him with a sixpence,
    And with a penny too;
He made a cake of rainbows,
    And baked it in the dew.

The stars he caught for raisins,
    The sun for candied peel,
The moon he broke for spices
    And ground it on a wheel.

He stirred the cake with sunbeams,
    And mixed it faithfully
With all the happy wishings
    That come to you and me.

He iced it with a moonbeam,
    He patterned it with play,
And sprinkled it with star dust
    From off the Milky Way.

Mary Gilmore

THE MOON-CHILD

A little lonely child am I
  That have not any soul:
God made me as the homeless wave,
  That has no goal.

A seal my father was, a seal
  That once was man;
My mother loved him tho' he was
  'Neath mortal ban.

He took a wave and drownèd her,
  She took a wave and lifted him:
And I was born where shadows are
  In sea-depths dim.

All through the sunny blue-sweet hours
  I swim and glide in waters green:
Never by day the mournful shores
  By me are seen.

But when the gloom is on the wave
  A shell unto the shore I bring:
And then upon the rocks I sit
  And plaintive sing.

I have no playmate but the tide
  The seaweed loves with dark brown eyes:
The night-waves have the stars for play,
  For me but sighs.

Fiona Macleod

THE SPLENDOUR FALLS

The splendour falls on castle walls
    And snowy summits old in story:
The long light shakes across the lakes,
    And the wild cataract leaps in glory.
Blow, bugle, blow, set the wild echoes flying,
Blow, bugle; answer, echoes, dying, dying,
      dying.

O hark, O hear! how thin and clear,
    And thinner, clearer, farther going!
O sweet and far from cliff and scar
    The horns of Elfland faintly blowing!
Blow, let us hear the purple glens replying:
Blow, bugle; answer, echoes, dying, dying,
      dying.

O love, they die in yon rich sky,
    They faint on hill or field or river:
Our echoes roll from soul to soul,
    And grow for ever and for ever
Blow, bugle, blow, set the wild echoes flying,
And answer, echoes, answer, dying, dying,
      dying.

Alfred, Lord Tennyson

from GANDERFEATHER'S GIFT

I was just a little thing
  When a fairy came and kissed me;
Floating in upon the light
Of a haunted summer night,
Lo, the fairies came to sing
Pretty slumber songs and bring
  Certain boons that else had missed me.
From a dream I turned to see
What those strangers brought for me,
  When that fairy up and kissed me —
  Here, upon this cheek, he kissed me!

Simmerdew was there, but she
  Did not like me altogether;
Daisybright and Turtledove,
Pilfercurds and Honeylove,
Thistleblow and Amberglee
On that gleaming, ghostly sea
  Floated from the misty heather,
And around my trundle-bed
Frisked, and looked, and whispering said —
  Solemnlike and all together:
  "*You* shall kiss him, Ganderfeather!"

Eugene Field

10

GOBLIN STAIRS

Goblin wood has creepy stairs
  And twisty ti-tree thickets,
And Goblin men as shy as hares,
  And chirpy-brown as crickets.

I put on my scarlet coat
  And scarlet cap-a-bobbin.
For, if they see me there, I thought,
  They'll take me for a robin.

Down the Goblin Stairs I fled
  To see the Goblin people,
The little men in caps of red,
  As peaky as a steeple.

Goblin wood has Goblin snares
  And Goblin ti-tree in it.
When I went down the Goblin Stairs,
  I didn't stay a minute.

Annie R. Rentoul

WHEN I WAS SIX

When I was only six years old,
  Heigh-ho! for Folly O!
I wandered in a fairy fold,
  Heigh holly! to and fro.

I rode upon a blossom's back
  Up hill and over sea;
And all the little pixie pack
  For fun would follow me.

O, golden was the gown I wore
  Of buttercups and air,
And twenty diamond stars or more
  Were pinned upon my hair.

All day I chased the laughing sky
  Above the busy town,
But when the moon unwinked her eye,
  Ho, ho! I hurried down.

And then within the baby's shoe
  I hid my lady's pearls.
From maid to merry maid I flew
  And knotted all their curls.

And when the children were abed,
  I tapped the window-pane,
And laughed as someone softly said:
  "Whist! goblins there again!"

Ho ho! I flitted here and there
  Amid my elfin band,
While on the green, in frolic fair,
  We tripped it hand in hand.

As air and moonlight I was free
  Within that fairy fold,
For all the world belonged to me
  When I was six years old.

Zora Cross

BLUE PEOPLE

blue people of air
　　spin fire in the sky
till the wind takes hold,
　　fanning fire across the sky
like wild hair

Kerry Leves

LOOKING-GLASS RIVER

Smooth it glides upon its travel,
  Here a wimple, there a gleam —
    O the clean gravel!
    O the smooth stream!

Sailing blossoms, silver fishes,
  Paven pools as clear as air —
    How a child wishes
    To live down there!

We can see our coloured faces
  Floating on the shaken pool
    Down in cool places,
    Dim and very cool;

Till a wind or water wrinkle,
  Dipping marten, plumping trout,
    Spreads in a twinkle
    And blots all out.

See the rings pursue each other;
  All below grows black as night,
    Just as if mother
    Had blown out the light!

Patience, children, just a minute —
  See the spreading circles die;
    The stream and all in it
    Will clear by-and-by.

Robert Louis Stevenson

ALMS IN AUTUMN

Spindlewood, spindlewood, will you lend me pray,
A little flaming lantern to guide me on my way?
The fairies all have vanished from the
    meadow and the glen,
And I would fain go seeking till I find them
    once again.
Lend me now a lantern that I may bear a light,
To find the hidden pathway in the darkness
    of the night.

Ashtree, ashtree, throw me, if you please,
Throw me down a slender bunch of
    russet-gold keys,
I fear the gates of Fairyland may all be shut so fast
That nothing but your magic keys will ever
    take me past.
I'll tie them to my girdle and as I go along,
My heart will find a comfort in the tinkle of
    their song.

Hollybush, hollybush, help me in my task,
A pocketful of berries is all the alms I ask,
A pocketful of berries to thread on golden strands,
(I would not go a-visiting with nothing
    in my hands).
So fine will be the rosy chains, so gay,
    so glossy bright,
They'll set the realms of Fairyland
    all dancing with delight.

Rose Fyleman

ECHO

How see you Echo? When she calls I see
Her pale face looking down through some
   great tree,
Whose world of green is like a moving sea,
That shells re-echo.
I see her with a white face like a mask,
That vanishes to come again; damask
Her cheek, but deeply pale,
Her eyes are green,
With a silver sheen,
And she mocks the thing you ask.
"O Echo!" (hear the children calling)
   "are you there?". . .
"Where?". . .

When the wind blows over the hill,
She hides with a vagrant will,
And call you may loud, and call you may long,
She lays finger on lip
     when the winds are strong,
And for all your pains she is still.
But when young plants spring,
   and the chiff-chaffs sing,
And the scarlet capped woodpecker
   flies through the vale,
She is out all day,
Through the fragrant May,

To babble and tattle her Yea and Nay.
"O Echo!" (still the children call) "Where are you?
where?" . . .
"Air . . ."

Viscountess Grey

THE BUTTERFLY

The Butterfly, an idle thing,
Nor honey makes, nor yet can sing,
  As do the bee and bird;
Nor does it, like the prudent ant,
Lay up the grains for times of want,
  A wise and cautious hoard.

My youth is but a summer's day:
Then like the bee and ant I'll lay
  A store of learning by;
And though from flower to flower I rove,
My stock of wisdom I'll improve,
  Nor be a butterfly.

Adelaide O'Keefe

HIST WHIST

hist whist
little ghostthings
tip-toe
twinkle-toe

little twitchy
witches and tingling
goblins
hob-a-nob   hob-a-nob

little hoppy happy
toad in tweeds
tweeds
little itchy mousies

with scuttling
eyes   rustle and run
  and
hidehidehide
whisk

whisk   look out for the
old woman
with the wart on her
  nose
what she'll do to yer
nobody knows

for she knows the
  devil   ooch
the devil   ouch
the devil
ach   the great

green
dancing
devil
devil

devil
devil

wheeEEE

e. e. cummings

26

WITCHES' CHARMS

The weather is fair, the wind is good
Up, dame, on your horse of wood!
Or else tuck up your grey frock,
And saddle your goat or your green cock,
And make his bridle a ball of thread
To roll up how many miles you have rid.
Quickly come away,
For we all stay.

The owl is abroad, the bat and the toad,
And so is the cat-a-mountain;
The ant and the mole sit both in a hole,
And the frog peeps out of the fountain,
The dogs they do bay, and the timbrels play.
The spindle is now a-turning;
The moon it is red, and the stars have fled,
But the sky is a-burning.

Ben Jonson

from BOY DREAMS

I was a Merman once,
In the gloom of the amber-tinted seas,
With the brown tang clinging
    about my knees,
With a coral house, and a crab to ride,
Who pranced, and who ambled
    from side to side;
I wooed a Mermaid with emerald hair,
Dragged the fierce sea-serpent
    from out his lair,
With his flaming tongue and his awful might,
And I slew him — easy — in open fight!
I had strings of pearls, white as frozen milk,
That were strung for me on sea-spider's silk;
And I never pined for the upper skies,
Whose blue came down
    in the dead men's eyes,
Drowned men with the salt
    on their blackened lips,
Who slid, drifting in,
    from the wrecks of ships;
But I took the gold from the belts of all,
To pave the road to my coral hall.

M. Forrest

THE FAIRIES

Up the airy mountain,
  Down the rushy glen,
We daren't go a-hunting
  For fear of little men;
Wee folk, good folk,
  Trooping all together;
Green jacket, red cap,
  And white owl's feather!

Down along the rocky shore
  Some make their home,
They live on crispy pancakes
  Of yellow tide-foam;
Some in the reeds
  Of the black mountain-lake,
With frogs for their watch-dogs,
  All night awake.

High on the hill-top
  The old King sits;
He is now so old and gray
  He's nigh lost his wits.

With a bridge of white mist
  Columbkill he crosses,
On his stately journeys
  From Slieveleague to Rosses;
Or going up with music
  On cold starry nights,
To sup with the Queen
  Of the gay Northern Lights.

They stole little Bridget
   For seven years long;
When she came down again
   Her friends were all gone.
They took her lightly back,
   Between the night and morrow,

They thought that she was fast asleep,
   But she was dead with sorrow.
They have kept her ever since
   Deep within the lake,
On a bed of flag-leaves,
   Watching till she wake.

By the craggy hill-side,
   Through the mosses bare,
They have planted thorn-trees
   For pleasure here and there.
Is any man so daring
   As to dig one up in spite,
He shall find the thornies set
   In his bed at night.

Up the airy mountain,
   Down the rushy glen,
We daren't go a-hunting
   For fear of little men;
Wee folk, good folk,
   Trooping all together;
Green jacket, red cap,
   And white owl's feather!

William Allingham

THE ROAD TO FAIRYLAND

Do you seek the road to Fairyland?
　I'll tell; it's easy, quite.
Wait till a yellow moon gets up
　O'er purple seas by night,
And gilds a shining pathway
　That is sparkling diamond bright
Then, if no evil power be nigh
　To thwart you, out of spite,
And if you know the very words
　To cast a spell of might,
You get upon a thistledown,
　And, if the breeze is right,
You sail away to Fairyland
　Along this track of light.

Ernest Thompson Seton

OVERHEARD ON A SALTMARSH

Nymph, nymph, what are your beads?

Green glass, goblin. Why do you stare at them?

Give them me.

                              No.

Give them me. Give them me.

                              No.

Then I will howl all night in the reeds,
Lie in the mud and howl for them.

Goblin, why do you love them so?

They are better than stars or water,
Better than voices of winds that sing,
Better than any man's fair daughter,
Your green glass beads on a silver ring.

Hush, I stole them out of the moon.

Give me your beads, I want them.

                              No.

I will howl in a deep lagoon
For your green glass beads, I love them so.
Give them me, Give them.

                              No.

Harold Monro

36

BY THE MOON

By the moon we sport and play,
With the night begins our day:
As we dance the dew doth fall,
Trip it little urchins all:

Lightly as the little bee,
Two by two, and three by three:
And about go we, and about go we.

Then I get upon a fly,
She carries me above the sky:
And trip and go.

When a dew drop falleth down,
And doth light upon my crown,
Then I shake my head and skip,
And about I trip.
Two by two, and three by three:
And about go we, and about go we.

Thomas Ravenscroft

THE FAIRY FROM
THE APPLE-SEED

O apple-seed I planted in a silly shallow
  place
In a bowl of wrought silver,
  with Sangamon earth within it,
O baby tree that came, without an apple
  on it,
A tree that grew a tiny height, but
  thickened an apace,
With bossy glossy arms, and leaves of
  trembling lace.

One night the trunk was rent,
  and the heavy bowl rocked round,
The boughs were bending here and there,
  with a curious locust sound,
And a tiny dryad came, from out the doll
  tree,
And held the boughs in ivory hands,
And waved her black hair round,
And climbed, and ate with merry words
The sudden fruit it bore.
And in the leaves she hides and sings
And guards my study door.

She guards it like a watchdog true
And robbers run away.
Her eyes are lifted spears all night,
But dove-eyes in the day.

And she is stranger, stronger
Than the funny human race.
Lovelier her form, and holier her face.
She feeds me flowers and fruit
With a quaint grace.
She dresses in the apple-leaves
As delicate as lace.
This girl that came from Sangamon earth
In a bowl of silver bright
From an apple-seed I planted in a silly
      shallow place.

Vachel Lindsay

THE SLEEP SEA

The Sleep-Sea calls
  To my mariner bold,
"Come hither to me,
  The night is cold.

"Mine arms are wide
  And my deeps are kind,
For never to me
  Comes stormy wind.

"My rocks are dreams,
  Where, a-drift, a-drift,
My cradle-ship
  May fall and lift.

"My shoals are isles
  Of slumbery sweets
Where never a wave
  In anger beats."

Do shut thine eyes
  My mariner bold:
The Sleep-Sea calls,
  The night is cold.

Mary Gilmore

THE WATER LADY

Alas, the moon should ever beam
To show what man should never see!
I saw a maiden on a stream,
And fair was she!

I stayed awhile, to see her throw
Her tresses back, that all beset
The fair horizon of her brow
With clouds of jet.

I stayed a little while to view
Her cheek, that wore in place of red
The bloom of water, tender blue,
Daintily spread.

I stayed to watch, a little space,
Her parted lips if she would sing;
The waters closed above her face
With many a ring.

And still I stayed a little more
Alas! she never comes again;
I throw my flowers from the shore,
And watch in vain.

I know my life will fade away,
I know that I must vainly pine,
For I am made of mortal clay,
But she's divine!

Thomas Hood

GOSSIP

"Trains are all the fashion,"
  Said the fairy in the tree.
"They'll catch upon the brambles
When we go for moonlight scrambles,
  And then where shall we be?"

"At the caterpillar's wedding,"
  Said the pixie in the moss,
"The dewdrops were so fizzy
That all the guests went dizzy.
  The Queen was very cross."

"The weather clerk's gone crazy,"
  Said the brownie in the fern,
"And all the kinds of weather
Have got mixed up together.
  They don't know where to turn!"

"It's nothing else but temper,"
  Said the nixie in the pool;
"They've hung him on a spire
With a little bit of wire
  And left him there to cool."

"But have you heard the latest?"
  Said the goblin in the ditch.
"Young Puck has changed the dresses
Of the little twin princesses,
  And they don't know which is which!"

Rose Fyleman

FAERY SONG

Shed no tear! Oh shed no tear!
The flower will bloom another year.
Weep no more! Oh weep no more!
Young buds sleep in the root's white core.
Dry your eyes! Oh dry your eyes!
For I was taught in Paradise
To ease my breast of melodies —
    Shed no tear.

Overhead! look overhead!
'Mong the blossoms white and red —
Look up, look up. I flutter now
On this flush pomegranate bough.
See me! 'tis this silvery bill
Ever cures the good man's ill.
Shed no tear! Oh shed no tear!
The flower will bloom another year.
Adieu, Adieu! I fly, adieu!
I vanish in the heaven's blue —
    Adieu, Adieu!

John Keats

EVERY FAIRY GODMOTHER

Oh, every fairy godmother must have
    a lot to plan,
She can't lie low and rest awhile as other
    fairies can;
For soon the wind comes rushing by, and
    sounding this alarm —
"Oh, some one wants a godmother
    to help her out of harm!"

Still, every fairy godmother must have
    a lot of fun
In tracking down a god-daughter
    (and sometimes a godson);
For she may find her with a broom
    in ever such distress;
And, oh, what fun to wave a wand
    and make her a Princess!

Agnes Grozier Herbertson

PUK-WUDJIES

They live 'neath the curtain
   Of fir woods and heather,
And never take hurt in
   The wildest of weather,
But best they love Autumn —
   she's brown as themselves —
And they are the brownest
   of all the brown elves;
     When loud sings the West Wind,
     The bravest and best wind,
And puddles are shining in all the cart ruts,
     They turn up the dead leaves,
     The russet and red leaves,
Where squirrels have taught them
     to look out for nuts!

The hedge-cutters hear them
   Where berries are glowing,
The scythe circles near them
   At time of the mowing,
But most they love woodlands
   when Autumn's winds pipe
And all through the cover the beechnuts
   are ripe,

     And great spikey chestnuts,
     The biggest and best nuts,
Blown down in the ditches,
   fair windfalls lie cast,
     And no tree begrudges

The little Puk-Wudjies
A pocket of acorns, a handful of mast!

So should you be roaming
    Where branches are sighing,
When up in the gloaming
    The moon-wrack is flying,
And hear through the darkness
    again and again,
What's neither the wind nor
    the spatter of rain —
        A flutter, a flurry,
        A scuffle, a scurry,
A bump like the rabbits' that bump
    on the ground,
        A patter, a bustle
        Of small things that rustle,
You'll know the Puk-Wudjies
    are somewhere around!

Patrick R. Chalmers

Ida Rentoul Outhwaite

from GOBLIN MARKET

. . . Backwards up the mossy glen
Turned and trooped the goblin men,
With their shrill repeated cry,
"Come buy, come buy."

When they reached where Laura was
They stood stock still upon the moss,
Leering at each other,
Brother with queer brother;
Signalling each other,
Brother with sly brother.
One set his basket down,
One reared his plate;
One began to weave a crown
Of tendrils, leaves, and rough nuts brown
(Men sell not such in any town);
One heaved the golden weight
Of dish and fruit to offer her:

"Come buy, come buy," was still their cry.
Laura stared but did not stir,
Longed but had no money:
The whisk-tailed merchant bade her taste
In tones as smooth as honey,
The cat-faced purr'd,
The rat-paced spoke a word
Of welcome, and the snail-paced even was heard;
One parrot-voiced and jolly
Cried "Pretty Goblin" still for "Pretty Polly"; —
One whistled like a bird.

But sweet-tooth Laura spoke in haste:
"Good folk, I have no coin;
To take were to purloin:
I have no copper in my purse,
I have no silver either,
And all my gold is on the furze
That shakes in windy weather
Above the rusty heather."
"You have much gold upon your head,"
They answered all together:
"Buy from us with a golden curl."
She clipped a precious golden lock,
She dropped a tear more rare than pearl,
Then sucked their fruit globes fair or red:
Sweeter than honey from the rock,
Stronger than man-rejoicing wine,
Clearer than water flowed that juice;
She never tasted such before,
How should it cloy with length of use?
She sucked and sucked and sucked the more
Fruits which that unknown orchard bore;
She sucked until her lips were sore;
Then flung the emptied rinds away
But gathered up one kernel-stone,
And knew not was it night or day
As she turned home alone . . .

Christina Rossetti

THE FAIRY

Said Ann to Matilda: "I wish that we knew
If what we've been reading of fairies be true.
Do you think that the poet himself had
    a sight of
The fairies he here does so prettily write of?
O what a sweet sight if he really had seen
The graceful Titania, the Fairyland Queen!
If I had such dreams, I would sleep
    a whole year;
I would not wish to wake while a fairy
    was near. —
Now I'll fancy that I in my sleep
   have been seeing
A fine little delicate lady-like being,
Whose steps and whose motions
   so light were and airy,
I knew at one glance that she must be a fairy.

Her eyes they were blue, and her fine
    curling hair
Of the lightest of browns, her complexion
   more fair
Than I e'er saw a woman's; and then
   for her height,
I verily think that she measur'd not quite
Two feet, yet so justly proportion'd withal,
I was almost persuaded to think she was tall.
Her voice was the little thin note of a sprite —
There — d'ye think I have made out
    a fairy aright?

You'll confess, I believe, I've not done
    it amiss."
"Pardon me," said Matilda, "I find in all this
Fine description, you've only your young
    sister Mary
Been taking a copy of here for a fairy."

Charles Lamb

NIGHT PIECE

Her eyes the glow-worm lend thee,
The shooting stars attend thee;
   And the elves also,
   Whose little eyes glow
Like the sparks of fire, befriend thee.

No Will-o'-the-Wisp mislight thee,
Nor snake or slow-worm bite thee;
   But on, on thy way,
   Not making a stay,
Since ghost there's none to affright thee.

Let not the dark thee cumber;
What though the moon does slumber?
   The stars of the night
   Will lend thee their light,
Like tapers clear, without number . . .

Robert Herrick

Acknowledgements

The publishers are grateful for the assistance given by the various copyright holders. Every effort has been made to trace them and the original sources but in a few cases this has proved impossible. We would be interested to hear from any copyright holders not acknowledged here.

cummings, e. e.; *hist whist,* taken from *Complete Poems,* permission given by Granada Publishing Ltd.

Fyleman, Rose; *Alms in Autumn* and *Gossip,* permission given by the Society of Authors as the literary representative of the Estate of Rose Fyleman.

Gilmore, Mary; *The Sleep Sea* and *The Fairy Man,* permission given by Angus & Robertson Publishers on behalf of the Public Trust Office, NSW.

Leves, Kerry; *Blue People,* first published in the NSW Department of Education *School Magazine,* permission given by Dorothy M. Leves on behalf of Kerry Leves.

Rentoul, Annie; *Goblin Stairs,* taken from *Elves and Fairies,* permission given by Lady Wendy Martin, Miss Jean Isobel Rentoul and Mr John Laurence Rentoul.

The Illustrations

Most of the illustrations included in this book have been drawn from two books, both first published in limited editions. The pictures on pages ii, 3, 11, 13, 19, 25, 28, 31, 35, 43, 45 and 53 come from *Elves and Fairies.* Those on pages 7, 8, 17, 21, 37, 39, 47 and 49 come from *Fairyland.* The illustration on page 27 is from the original edition of *The Lady of the Blue Beads.*